P9-DBT-116

The Manger Is Empty

Other Books by Walter Wangerin, Jr.

As For Me and My House
The Book of the Dun Cow
The Book of Sorrows
Little Lamb, Who Made Thee?
Measuring the Days
A Miniature Cathedral
Miz Lil and the Chronicles of Grace
Mourning Into Dancing
The Orphean Passages
Ragman and Other Cries of Faith
Reliving the Passion

The Manger Is Empty

Walter Wangerin, Jr.

A CROSSINGS®
BOOK CLUB EDITION

 For information address Crossings Book Club, 401 Franklin Avenue, Garden City, NY 11530

ISBN 0-7394-0629-9

To my daughter, Mary,
and to Dee Dee Lawrence

The Manger Is Empty

The Manger Is Empty

1.

My daughter cried on Christmas Eve. What should I say to the heart of my daughter? How should I comfort her?

Her name is Mary. She's a child. She wasn't crying the tears of disillusionment, as adults do when they've lost the spirit of the season. And she trusts me. I do not lie. My Mary is easily able to throw her arms around me in the kitchen and to hang on with a hug—proving that she trusts me. Neither, then, was she weeping the tears of an oversold imagination that Christmas Eve. She hadn't dreamed a gift too beautiful to be real, nor had she expected my love to buy better than my purse.

Nor was she sick. Nor was she hungry for any physical thing.

No, Mary was longing for Odessa Williams, that old black lady. Mary was longing for her life. That's why she was crying.

Too suddenly the child had come to the limits of the universe. A casket. She stood at the edge of emptiness and had no other response than tears. She turned to me and wept against my breast, and I am her father. And should I be mute before such tears? What should I say to the heart of my daughter Mary?

* * *

We have a custom in our congregation: always we gather on the Sunday evening before Christmas, bundled and hatted and happy, and we go, then, out into the sharp December darkness to sing carols. Down the streets of the city we go, the children bounding forward, adults all striding behind, chattering, making congenial noises, puffing ghosts of breath beneath the streetlights, laughing and glad for the company. Does anyone think it will snow? It's cold enough to snow, and the air is still, and the stars are already a snow-dust in heaven.

It's a common, communal custom. You do it too?

We crowd on the porches of the old folks. The children feel a squealing excitement because they think we're about to astonish Mrs. Moody in her parlor by our sudden appearing—carols from the out-of-doors, you know. She'll be so-o-o-o surprised! So they giggle and roar a marvelous *Hark!* with their faces pressed against her window: *Hark! The herald angels sing, glory to the newborn king—*

Mrs. Moody turns on her porch light, then opens her curtains, and there she is, shaking her head and smiling, and the children fairly burst with glee. They can hardly stand it, to be so good. She turns on her porch light, and here we are, fifteen, maybe twenty of us, spilling down her steps into the little yard, lifting our faces, lifting our voices—doing silly things, like lifting our key-rings to the refrain of "Jingle Bells" and making a perfect, rhythmic jangle. Everybody's willing to be a kid. Nobody minds the cold tonight. The white faces among us are pinched with pink; the black ones (we are mostly black ones) frost, as though the cold were a white dust on our cheeks.

And down the street we go again, and so we sing for Mrs. Lander and Mrs. Smith and Mrs. Buckman and Mrs. DeWitt.

And though we can be silly, and though this is just an ordinary custom, yet we are no ordinary choir. No: many of us sing for "The Sounds of Grace," a choir of legitimate repute. And some of us have been blessed by God with voices the angels would weep to own.

For sometimes on that Sunday evening, by a decision that no one understands, Timmy Moore will begin a solo in a husky and generous tenor voice. *O holy night,* the young man starts to sing, and then we are all an audience, listening in a starry dark. *It is the night of the dear Savior's birth. Long lay the world,* sings Timmy Moore. We bow our heads. Mrs. DeWitt, on the inside of her window, bows her head. We are more than an audience. We are passengers. This strong voice is a sort of chariot, you know, able to carry us out of the streets of the city, through dark night, to the fields of shepherds far away. *Fall on your knees,* sings Timmy Moore, huge and strong, transported: *O hear the angel voices! O night divine! O night when Christ was born.* There is locomotive power in this, and truth, and utter conviction, and we can scarcely breathe. *O night! O night divine.*

So then, Timmy is silent. And what then? Why, then we all sing "Silent Night." And then occurs such a sweet and delicate wonder that Mrs. DeWitt looks up with the astonishment that the children had expected at first, but which none of the children notice now, for they are caught in the wonder too. Mrs. DeWitt looks up and starts to cry. She covers her mouth with an aged hand, and she cries.

For on the third verse of "Silent Night," Dee Dee Lawrence, that blinking, innocent child, soars high and high above us all on a descant so beautiful it can break your heart. Dee Dee simply flies, high and light, precise, to the stars themselves, to the crystal sphere of heaven, and we are singing too, but we have forgotten we sing. Dee Dee is the winter's bird, singing: *Son of God, love's pure light, Radiant beams from thy holy face—* And when that child has reached the crystal sphere, with the wing of her music she touches it, and all the round sky rings. The night is alive. This is the wonder that catches us all. *With the dawn of redeeming grace,* sings Dee Dee Lawrence, and then she sinks to the earth again: *Jesus, Lord, at thy birth,* descending, descending—innocent, I think, of the thing she has just accomplished—finding her place in the midst of earthly voices again. *Jesus, Lord, at thy birth.* And she is done. And we are done. We move in quietness to the next house.

Dee Dee Lawrence has a round, milk-chocolate face and an

oriental cast to her eyes. Her beauty is not remarkable. Until she sings.

As we walk to the next house, we become aware that we, with Mrs. DeWitt, have been crying. That's why we are quiet. The tears are icy on our cheeks.

But these are good, contemplative tears. They are not like the tears my Mary cried on Christmas Eve.

And so it was that on Sunday evening, the twentieth of December, 1981, we kept our custom and went out caroling. Mary was seven years old then. Dee Dee was eight. Timmy was with us, and the Hildreth children. Most of the children's choir, in fact, had come along. The night was not much different from those that went before—except for this, that when we had finished our round of houses we went to St. Mary's Hospital to sing for several members who were patients at Christmas time. We divided into three groups. As pastor, I myself led a handful of children to the room of Odessa Williams because her condition was worse than the others.

It was Odessa Williams who made the night different.

The children had never laid eyes on her before. When they crept into the ward and saw her cadaverous body, they were speechless for a while. Scared, I think. Mary's blue eyes grew very large, and I felt pity for her.

Well, I knew what to expect, but Mary didn't. I had been visiting the woman for several years now—first in her apartment, where she'd been housebound, then in the nursing home—and I had watched the wasting of Odessa.

Two years ago she had been a strapping tall woman of strong ways, strong opinions, and very strong affections. Fiercely she had loved the church that she couldn't actually attend. She'd kept abreast of congregational activities by telephone, by a gossip-system, by bulletins and newsletters and friends—and by me. She pumped me for information every time I visited her, puffing an endless chain of cigarettes, striding about her apartment in crushed slippers, waving her old black arms in strong declaration of the things she thought I ought to do and the things I ought not, as pastor, to be doing.

I had learned, for my own protection, to check her mouth as soon as I entered her room. If the woman wore dentures, she was mad: she wanted her words to click with clarity, to snap and hiss with a precision equal to her anger. Mad at me, she needed teeth. But if she smiled a toothless smile on me, then I knew that her language would be soft and I had her approval—that week. She was particularly fierce regarding her children, the choir, the "Sounds of Grace," though she had never heard them sing. She loved them. She swelled with a grand, maternal love for them. And if ever I had not, by her estimate, done right by these children, the teeth in the mouth of Odessa Williams were the flashing, clacking weapons of an avenging angel.

It will be understood why I was never able to persuade the woman to stop smoking. Even in the nursing home she continued to smoke. But the disease that kept her housebound and sent her to the nursing home was cancer.

Cancer, finally, had laid her in the hospital.

And it was cancer that frightened the children when they crept around her bed on Sunday night, coming to sing carols to her. It put the odor of warm rot in the air. It had wasted Odessa to bone.

Mary and Dee Dee and Timmy and the others tried to touch nothing in the little space, not the bed, not the wall behind them. They grew solemn, unable to take their eyes from the form before them. One little lamp shed an orange light on the hollows of Odessa's face, sunken cheeks and sunken temples and deep, deep eyes. The lids on her eyes were thin as onion skin, half-closed; and her flesh was dry like parchment; and the body that once was strapping now resembled broomsticks in her bed—skinny arms on a caven stomach, fingers as long as chalk. And who could tell if the woman was breathing?

Mary stood across the bed from me, not looking at me, gazing down at Odessa. Mary's eyes kept growing larger.

So I whispered to all of them, "Sing." But they shuffled instead.

"What's this?" I whispered. "Did you lose your voices? Do you think she won't like it?"

"We think she won't hear," said Mary.

"No, no, sing the same as you always do," I said. "Sing for Miz Williams."

Well, and so they did, that wide-eyed ring of children, though it was a pitiful effort at first. "Away in a Manger," like nursery kids suspicious of their audience. But by the time the cattle were lowing, the children had found comfort in the sound of their own voices and began to relax. Moreover, Odessa had opened her eyes, and there was light in there, and she had begun to pick out their faces, and I saw that Mary was returning Odessa's look with a fleeting little smile. So then they harked it with herald angels, and they found in their bosoms a first noel that other angels did say, and then a marvelous thing began to happen: Odessa Williams was frowning—frowning and nodding, frowning with her eyes squeezed shut, frowning, you see, with fierce pleasure, as though she were chewing a delicious piece of meat. So then Mary and all the children were grinning, because they knew instinctively what the frown of an old black woman meant.

Odessa did not have her dentures in.

And the marvelous thing that had begun could only grow more marvelous still.

For I whispered, "Dee Dee," and the innocent child glanced at me, and I said, "Dee Dee, 'Silent Night.'"

Dear Dee Dee! That girl, as dark as the shadows around her, stroked the very air as though it were a chime of glass. (Dee

Dee, I love you!) So high she soared on her crystal voice, so long she held the notes, that the rest of the children hummed and harmonized all unconsciously, and they began to sway together. "Round yon virgin, mother and child. . . ."

Odessa's eyes flew open to see the thing that was happening around her. She looked, then she raised her long, long arms; and then lying on her back, the old woman began to direct the music. By strong strokes she lifted Dee Dee Lawrence. She pointed the way, and Dee Dee trusted her, so Dee Dee sang a soprano descant higher and braver than she had ever sung before. Impossible! Stroke for stroke with imperious arms, Odessa Williams gathered all her children and urged them to fly, and sent them on a celestial flight to glory, oh! These were not children anymore. These were the stars. Their voices ascended on fountains of light to become the very hosts of heaven—so high, so bright and holy and high. *Jesus, Lord, at thy birth!* So beautiful.

And then that woman brought them down again, by meek degrees to the earth again, and to this room and to her bedside; and there they stood, perfectly still, smiling in silence and waiting. How could anyone move immediately after such a wonder?

Nor did Odessa disappoint them. For then she began, in a low and smoky voice, to preach.

"Oh, children—you my choir," Odessa whispered. "Oh, choir—you my children for sure. An' listen me," she whispered intently. She caught them one by one on the barb of her eye. "Ain' no one stand in front of you for goodness, no! You the bes', babies. You the absolute *best.*"

The children gazed at her, and the children believed her completely: they were the best. And my Mary, too, believed what she was hearing, heart and soul.

"Listen me," Odessa said. "When you sing, wherever you go to sing, look down to the front row of the people who come to hear you sing. There's alluz an empty seat there. See it?" The children nodded. They saw it. "Know what that empty space is?" The children shook their heads. "It's me," she said, and they nodded. "It's me," she whispered in the deep orange light. " 'Cause I alluz been with you, children. An' whenever you sing, I'm goin' to be with you still. An' you know how I can say such a mackulous thing?" They waited to know. She lowered her voice, and she told them. "Why, 'cause we in Jesus," she whispered the mystery. "Babies, babies, we be in the hand of Jesus, old ones, young ones, and us and you together. Jesus, he hold us in his hand, and ain' no one goin' to snatch us out. Jesus, he don' never let one of us go. Never. Not ever—"

So spoke Odessa, and then she fell silent. So said the woman with such conviction and such fierce love, that the children rolled tears from their open eyes, and they were not ashamed. They reached over and patted the bones of her body beneath the blankets.

Mary's eyes too were glistening. The woman had won my daughter. In that incandescent moment, Mary had come to love Odessa Williams. She slipped her soft hand toward the bed and touched the tips of Odessa's fingers, and she smiled and cried at once. For this is the power of a wise love wisely expressed: to transfigure a heart, suddenly, forever.

But neither were these like the tears that Mary wept on Christmas Eve.

2.

On Tuesday, the twenty-second of December, Odessa Williams died.

It had been a long time coming, but was quick when it came. She died in her sleep and went to God without her dentures.

Quick when it came, I say: Odessa left us little time to mourn for her. Gaines Funeral Home had less than a day to prepare her body, because the wake would take place on Wednesday evening. The funeral itself had to be scheduled for Thursday morning. There was no alternative. Friday was Christmas Day; Saturday and Sunday were the weekend; Gaines would be closed for three days straight, and Monday was too far away to make Odessa wait for burial. She would be buried, then, on Christmas Eve Day.

And I, for my own part, was terribly distracted by a hectic week. This was the very crush of the season, you see, with a children's pageant and extra services to prepare. My pastoral duty was already doubled; Odessa's funeral tripled it. So I rushed from labor to labor, more pastor than father, more worker than wise.

Not brutally, but somewhat busily at lunch on Wednesday, I mentioned to my children that Miz Williams had died. They were eating soup. This was not an unusual piece of news in our household: the congregation had its share of elderly.

I scarcely noticed, then, that Mary stopped eating and stared at her bowl of soup.

I wiped my mouth and rose from the table.

"Dad?"

I was trying to remember what time the children should be at church to rehearse the Christmas program. Timing was everything. I wanted to give them a last instruction before I left.

"Dad?"

One thirty! "Listen—Mom will drive you to church at one fifteen. Can you all be ready then?"

"Dad?"

"Mary, what?" She was still staring at the soup, large eyes lost behind her hair.

"Is it going to snow tomorrow?" she said.

"What? I don't know. How would I know that?"

"It shouldn't snow," she said.

"You always wanted snow at Christmas."

In a tiny voice she whispered, "I want to go to the funeral."

Well, then that was it: she was considering what to wear against the weather. I said, "Fine," and left.

Thursday came grey and hard and cold and windless. It grudged the earth a little light and made no shadow. The sky was sullen, draining color from the grass and the naked trees. I walked to church in the morning.

We have a custom in our congregation: always, before a funeral service begins, we set the casket immediately in front of the chancel and leave it open about an hour. People come for a final viewing of the body, friends who couldn't attend the wake, acquaintances on their way to work, strangers out of the past, memories, stories that will never be told. The dead one lies the same for all who gaze at her, infinitely patient. So people enter the church, and they creep up the aisle, and they look, and they think, and they leave again.

Soon some of the mourners remain. They keep their coats on, but they sit in the pews and wait. They remind me of winter birds on telephone wires, their plumage all puffed around them, their faces closed, contemplative.

And then, ten minutes before the service, I robe myself and stand in the back of the church to meet the greater flow of mourners. Last of all the family will arrive in limousines. I keep peeping out of the door to see whether the silent cars have slid to their places at the curb—

And so it was that on Christmas Eve at eleven in the morning I discovered Mary outside the door. In fact, she was standing on the sidewalk while her mother parked the car. She was staring at the sullen sky.

"Mary?" I said. "Are you coming in?"

She glanced at me. Then she whispered, "Dad?" as though the news were dreadful. "It's going to snow."

It looked very likely to snow. The air was still, the whole world bleak and waiting. I could have agreed with her.

"Dad?" she repeated more urgently, probing me with large eyes—but what was I supposed to do? "It's going to snow!" she said.

"Come in, Mary. We don't have time to talk. Come in."

She entered the church ahead of me and climbed the steps in the narthex, then she started up the aisle toward the casket. She was seven years old. She was determined. Though robed and ready to preach, and though people sat face-forward on either side, I followed her.

Mary hesitated as she neared the chancel—but then took a final step and stopped.

She looked down into the casket. "Oh, no," she murmured, and I looked to see what she was seeing.

Odessa's eyes seemed closed with glue, her lips too pale, her color another shade than her own, a false, woody color. Her skin seemed pressed into its patience. And the bridge of her nose suffered a set of glasses. Had Odessa worn glasses? Yes, sometimes. But these were perched on her face a little askew, so that one became aware of them for the first time. Someone else had put them there. What belonged to the lady any more, and what did not?

These were my speculations.

Mary had her own.

The child was reaching her hand toward the tips of Odessa's fingers, fingers like sticks of chalk; but she paused and didn't touch then. Suddenly she bent down and pressed her cheek to the fingers, then pulled back and stood erect.

"Dad!" she hissed. Mary turned and looked at me and did not blink but began to cry. "Dad!" she whispered, accusing, "It's going to snow, and Miz Williams is so cold." Immediately the tears were streaming down her face. "Dad!" she wept. "They can't put Miz Williams in the grave today. It's going to snow on her grave. It's going to snow on Miz Williams—"

All at once Mary stepped forward and buried her face in my robes. I felt the pressure of her forehead against my chest—and I was her father again, no pastor, and my own throat grew thick.

"Dad," sobbed Mary. "Dad, Dad, it's Christmas *Eve!*"

These were the tears. These were the tears my daughter cried at Christmas. What do I say to these tears? It is death my Mary met. It's the end of things. It's the knowledge that things *have* an end, good things, kind and blessed things, things new and rare and precious and their goodness doesn't save them; that love has an end; that people have an end; that Odessa Williams, that fierce old lady who seized the heart of my Mary and possessed it just four days ago, who was so real in dim light, waving her arms to the music of the children, that *she* has an end, has ended, is gone, is dead.

How do I comfort these tears? What do I say?

I said nothing.

I knelt down. I took my Mary's face between my hands but couldn't hold her gaze. I gathered her to myself and hugged her tightly, hugged her hard, hugged her until the sobbing passed from her body; and then I released her.

I watched her go back down the aisle like a poker soldier. She turned in a pew and sat with her mother. I saw that her lips were pinched into a terrible knot. No crying anymore. No questions anymore. Why should she ask questions when there were no answers given?

So: the funeral. And so: the sermon. And so I was the pastor again.

This was the text: "But there will be no gloom for her that was in anguish." The prophet Isaiah. It had seemed a perfect text, both for the season and for Odessa. "The people who walked in darkness have seen a great light," I read. That prophecy had come true in Jesus. It would become a truth again for the fierce old woman whose memorial this was. And for us too, since we were mourning now, but we would be celebrating tonight. I read: "For unto us a child is born, unto us a son is given—" *Christmas!* I said somewhere in my sermon. *Light is shining everywhere across the world, as light is shining first and perfectly in heaven! None who die in the Lord do die in darkness—*

But what were Isaiah and prophecy and all the sustaining truths of Christendom to my daughter Mary? She sat through the sermon with pinched lips and a sidelong stare. What was heaven to her? Nothing. Odessa had been something to her. You could touch and love Odessa. But Odessa was dead. The casket was closed. Death was something to her now, and maybe the only thing.

Later, at Oak Hill Cemetery, the people stood in great coats round the casket, shivering. My breath made ghosts in the air as I read of dust and ashes returning to dust and ashes. Mary said not a word nor held her mother's hand nor looked at me—except once.

When we turned from the grave she hissed, "Dad!" Her blue eyes flashing, she pointed at the ground. Then she pointed at the sky. At the roots of the grasses was a fine, white powder; in heaven was a darker powder coming down. It was snowing.

3.

We have several customs—in our church and in my family—on Christmas Eve: as to the church, we celebrate the evening always with a children's pageant of the birth of Jesus. There never was the pageant in which my children didn't participate. As for my family, we always open our Christmas presents after the pageant is over, when the glow is still upon us, when Thanne and I can watch the children and enjoy their joy. Nothing is dearer to me than the purity of their gladness then, the undiscordant music of their laughter then.

And nothing could grieve me more, than that one of my children should be sad and lose the blessings of these customs.

Therefore, I worried terribly for Mary all Thursday through. As it happened, she was to be *the* Mary of the pageant, the Virgin, the mother of the infant Jesus. At three in the afternoon I left church and went home to talk with her.

I found her alone in her bedroom, lying on the bed and gazing out the window, her chin on her wrists. Snow clouds caused a darkness within, but she'd left the lights off where she was.

I stood beside the bed and touched her. The pragmatic pastor was concerned whether this child could accomplish so public a role in so private a mood. The father simply wished he knew what his daughter was thinking.

"Mary," I said, "do you want us to get another Mary?"

She kept watching the snow come down. Slowly she shook her head. "No," she said. "I'm Mary."

I didn't think she'd understood me—and if she didn't, then my question must have sounded monstrous to her ears. "For the pageant, I mean," I said, "tonight."

But she repeated without the slightest variation, "I'm Mary."

Mary, Mary, so much Mary—but I wish you weren't sad. I wish I had a word for you. Forgive me. It isn't a kind world after all.

"You are Mary," I said. "I'll be with you tonight. It'll be all right."

We drove to church. The snow lay a loose inch on the ground. It swirled in snow-devils at the backs of the cars ahead of us. It held the grey light of the city near the earth, though this was now the night, and heaven was oblique in darkness. Surely, the snow covered Odessa's grave as well, a silent, seamless sheet.

These, I suppose, were Mary's thoughts, that the snow was cold on a new-dug grave. But Mary's thoughts confused with mine.

The rooms of the church were filled with light and noise, transfigured utterly from the low, funereal whispers of the morning. Black folk laughed. Parents stood in knots of conversation. Children darted, making ready for their glad performance, each in a different stage of dress, some in blue jeans, some in the robes of the shepherds two millennia and twenty lands away. Children were breathless and punchy. But Mary and I moved like spirits through this company, unnoticed and unnoticing. I was filled with her sorrow, while she seemed simply empty.

In time the wildness subsided. The actors huddled in their proper places. I sat with the congregation, two-thirds back on the right hand side. The lights in the sanctuary dimmed to darkness. The chancel glowed a yellow illumination. The pageant began, and soon my daughter stood with pinched lips, central to it all.

"My soul," said Mary, both Marys before a little Elizabeth—but she spoke so softly that few could hear, and my own soul suffered for her—"My soul," she murmured, "magnifies the Lord, and my spirit rejoices in God my Savior—"

And so: the child was surviving. But she was not rejoicing.

Some angels came and giggled and sang and left.

A decree went out.

Another song was sung.

And then three figures moved into the floodlit chancel: Joseph and Mary—and one other child, a sort of innkeeper-stage-manager who carried the manger, a wooden trough filled with old straw and a floppy doll in diapers.

The pageant proceeded, but I lost the greater part of it in watching my daughter.

For Mary stuck out her bottom lip and began to frown on the manger in front of her—to frown fiercely, not at all like the devout and beaming parent she was supposed to portray. At the *manger* she was staring, which stood precisely where Odessa's casket had sat that morning. She frowned so hard, blacking her eyes in such deep shadow, that I thought she would break into tears again, and my mind raced over things to do when she couldn't control herself any longer.

But Mary did not cry.

Instead, while shepherds watched over their flocks by night, my Mary played a part that no one had written into the script. Slowly she slipped her hand into the manger and touched the doll in diapers. She lifted its arm on the tip of her pointed finger, then let it drop. *What are you thinking, Mary?* All at once, as though she'd made a sudden decision, she yanked the doll out by its toes, and stood up, and clumped down the chancel steps, the doll like a dishrag at her side. People made mild, maternal sounds in their throats. The rhythm of a certain angel faltered. *Mary, where are you going? What are you doing?* I folded my hands at my chin and yearned to hold her, hide her, protect her from anything, from folly and from sorrow. But she carried the doll to the darkened sacristy on the right and disappeared through its door. *Mary? Mary!*

In a moment the child emerged carrying nothing at all. Briskly she returned to the manger, up three steps as light as air, and down she knelt, and she gazed upon the empty straw with her palms together like the first Mary after all, full of adoration. And her face—Mary, my Mary, your face was radiant then!

O Mary, how I love you!

Not suddenly, but with a rambling, stumbling charge, there was in the chancel a multitude of the proudest heavenly host, praising God and shouting, "Glory to God in the highest!" But Mary knelt unmoved among them, and her seven-year face was smiling, and there was the flash of tears upon her cheeks, but they were not unhappy, and the manger, open, empty, seemed the receiver of them.

"Silent night, holy night—" All of the children were singing. "All is calm, all is bright—" The deeper truck-rumble of older voices joined them. "Round yon virgin mother and child—" The whole congregation was singing. Candlelight was passing hand to hand. A living glow spread everywhere throughout the church. And then the shock of recognition, and the soft flight followed: Dee Dee Lawrence allowed her descant voice its high, celestial freedom, and she flew. "Holy infant, so tender and mild—" *Mary, what do you see? What do you know that your father could not tell you? Mary, mother of the infant Jesus, teach me too.*

"Sleep in heavenly peace—" Having touched the crystal

heaven Dee Dee descended. The congregation sighed. Everybody sang: "Sleep in heavenly peace."

Mary sat immediately beside me in the car as we drove home. A sifting snow made cones below the streetlights. It blew lightly across the windshield and closed us in a cotton privacy. I had been driving in silence.

Mary said, "Dad?"

I said, "What?"

She said, "Dad, Jesus wasn't in the manger. That wasn't Jesus. That was a doll." Ah, Mary, so you have the eyes of a realist now? And there is no pretending any more? It was a doll indeed. So death reveals realities—

"Dad?"

"What?"

She said, "Jesus, he doesn't *have* to be in the manger, does he? He goes back and forth, doesn't he? I mean, he came from heaven, and he was borned right here, but then he went back to heaven again, and because he came and went he's coming and going *all* the time—right?"

"Right," I whispered. Teach me, child. It is so good to hear you talk again.

"The manger is empty," Mary said. And then she said more gravely, "Dad, Miz Williams' box is empty too. I figured it out. We don't have to worry about the snow." She stared out the windshield a moment, then whispered the next thing as softly as if she were peeping at presents: "It's only a doll in her box. It's like a big doll, Dad, and we put it away today. I figured it out. If Jesus can cross, if Jesus can go across, then Miz Williams, she crossed the same way too, with Jesus—"

Jesus, he don't never let one of us go. Never.

"Dad?" said Mary, who could ponder so much in her heart. "Why are you crying?"

Babies, babies, we be in the hand of Jesus, old ones, young ones, us and you together. Jesus, he hold us in his hand, and ain' no one goin' to snatch us out. Jesus, he don't never let one of us go. Never. Not ever—

"Because I have nothing else to say," I said to her. "I haven't had the words for some time now."

"Dad?"

"What?"

"Don't cry. I can talk for both of us."

It always was; it always will be; it was in the fullness of time when the Christ child first was born; it was in 1981 when my daughter taught me the times and the crossing of times on Christmas Eve; it is in every celebration of Christ's own crossing; and it shall be forever—that this is the power of a wise love wisely expressed: to transfigure the heart, suddenly, forever.